WATER WORKS

150 YEARS OF LOUISVILLE WATER COMPANY

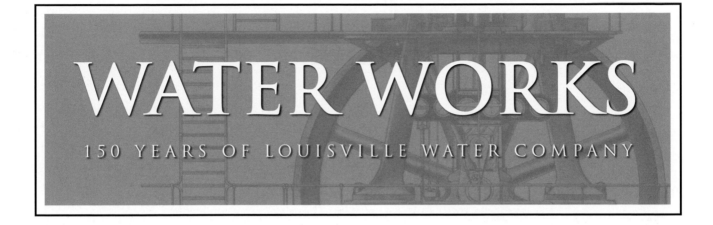

WATER WORKS

150 YEARS OF LOUISVILLE WATER COMPANY

BY KELLEY DEARING SMITH

BUTLER BOOKS

ISBN 978-1-935497-26-4

Printed in Canada

Author: Kelley Dearing Smith

Research Coordinator: Jay Ferguson

Book Designer: Scott Stortz

Published by:

Louisville Water Company
550 South Third Street
Louisville, KY 40202
(502) 569-3600
www.louisvillewater.com

in partnership with:

Butler Books
P.O. Box 7311
Louisville, KY 40207
(502) 897–9393
Fax (502) 897–9797
www.butlerbooks.com

CONTENTS

FOREWORD

GREG HEITZMAN

Louisville owes its birth to water. Founded in 1778, Louisville was settled by George Rogers Clark at the Falls of the Ohio River. For her first 75 years, an abundant, clean water source rolled past her door step, providing ample supply for a growing town.

By 1835, this river city needed a water works in order to expand beyond the riverbank and provide a cleaner supply of water. But, it would take over 20 years before the city's leaders were successful in establishing Louisville's Water Works. After six years of financing and construction, Louisville Water Company pumped its first gallon of water on October 16, 1860 to 512 customers. For the first time, Louisvillians were able to open their tap and the abundant Ohio River supply poured into their homes and businesses.

Now, 150 years later, the river is still an abundant source and Louisville Water is known for its safe, reliable, great-tasting water. Our continued success is due to a long-standing commitment to quality and innovation.

In the water industry, Louisville Water is widely known for its work in advancing public health through the development of water filtration. In 1895, Chief Engineer Charles Hermany and Chief Chemist George Warren Fuller oversaw experiments that revolutionized the science and engineering of clean water. This same technology has remained the standard of water treatment, worldwide, for the past 100 years.

Today, Louisville Water continues its leadership in innovation through the development of new water technology, known as Riverbank Filtration. It is only fitting that the world's largest Riverbank Filtration Tunnel is being placed in service this year, the 150th anniversary of our operations. This new technology will use the sands and gravels of the Ohio River aquifer to naturally filter the water in much the same way Hermany envisioned 125 years before.

Although the "Louisville Filtration Experiments" are known around the world, local citizens have come to know Louisville Water through its architecture, water quality and community involvement. From the beginning, the Louisville Water Tower and Pumping Station No. 1, designed by Theodore Scowden, served as the symbol of quality and innovation for generations of employees. The Crescent Hill Gatehouse and Reservoir, designed by Charles Hermany in 1878, are still in use today and remind us of the foundation set by our early leaders.

The pictorial history in "Water Works" covers our quest for pure water and the innovations that made it a reality, benefiting the citizens of Louisville, the region and, ultimately, the world. This book is dedicated to the employees, both past and present, who have contributed to our rich history.

Greg C. Heitzman

Greg Heitzman
President and CEO, Louisville Water Company
October 16, 2010

October 16, 1860

It was a cool, crisp fall day. Theodore Scowden and Charles Hermany anxiously awaited for a line of horse-drawn carriages to pull up to the reservoir that overlooked the towering structure on the banks of the Ohio River. The two engineers had spent years overseeing the construction of Louisville's Water Works. Today it would deliver the first supply of water.

The men were no doubt pleased at their accomplishment, yet likely did not fully realize they had created a landmark or that their work would be admired for years to come.

The history of Louisville Water Company illustrates its great impact on the city where it began. This is the story of Louisville's Water Works.

The two men had worked together in designing the Cleveland Water Works. Hermany's career with Louisville Water stretched over 50 years and his work helped define the company. Both men believed they were building more than a water works, they were building a community institution.

PRACTICAL BUT PLEASANT

Scowden believed that practical things should also be pleasant. He wrote that the Louisville facilities would be "regarded as the most elegant and commodious for water works purposes in the country."

The Pumping Station is Classical Revival style. The engine room and boiler rooms are in the form of a two-story temple with wings flanking the center piece and a portico entrance.

THEODORE SCOWDEN

CHARLES HERMANY

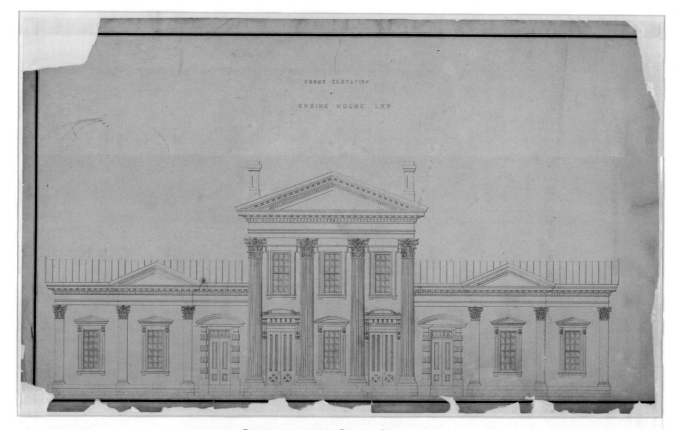

ORIGINAL DRAWING OF PUMPING STATION, 1858

The windows, sills and column bases of the Pumping Station are cast iron. The Corinthian capitals and entablature detail are terra-cotta.

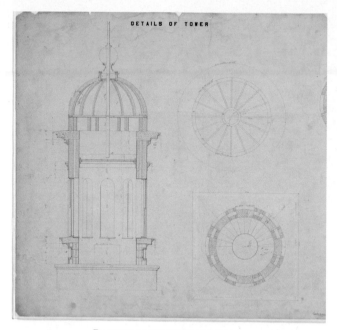

DETAILS OF TOWER

DRAWING OF THE TOP OF THE TOWER

STAND PIPE
TOWER
LOUISVILLE WATER C.

Scowden's vision for the Water Tower was a structure that would be "symmetrical and tasteful in appearance, as well as useful." He enclosed the standpipe with a 169-foot wooden tower. It is the oldest and most ornamental of its kind in the United States. The design in 1860 included a circular portico surrounding the base, ten Corinthian columns with a balustrade and pedestals over each column. A lighthouse-like look-out area capped the top. The original drawing shows urns atop the pedestals; instead, ten statues representing Ceres, Diana, Flora and The Horae (the seasons) were added in 1861 at a price of $271.75.

ORIGINAL DRAWING OF WATER TOWER, 1858

Scowden and Hermany envisioned a "park-like" setting for the facilities and called the landscape a place of "unrivaled beauty and effect." Their vision holds true today.

ORIGINAL RESERVOIR

The water company's original reservoir was atop a 90 foot cliff, overlooking the Ohio River Valley. The reservoir was a settling basin where mud and clay from the Ohio River water would settle before it was delivered to customers by gravity through water mains. (In 1860, the water company did not "treat" the water.) Once again, Scowden envisioned a working facility and place of attraction. A decorative fence, brick path and four cast-iron benches surrounded the reservoir. Scowden wrote that the reservoir could be a place for those "who may be in quest of fresh air, beautiful scenery and relaxation from the cares of business." Sitting on one of those cast-iron benches provided a view of a park Louisville Water built. The "Water Works Park," sitting along what is now River Road, included a fountain that shot water 100 feet in the air.

CONSTRUCTING THE ORIGINAL RESERVOIR

THREE MEN SIT ON A CAST-IRON BENCH AT THE ORIGINAL RESERVOIR, GAZING UPON WATER WORKS PARK.

ALTHOUGH BLURRY, THIS PHOTOGRAPH TAKEN FROM THE ORIGINAL RESERVOIR SHOWS WATER WORKS PARK AND ITS FOUNTAIN.
THE PUMPING STATION AND WATER TOWER ARE IN THE DISTANCE. PHOTOGRAPH CIRCA 1862.

THE ORIGINAL RESERVOIR BECAME A SWIMMING POOL

Louisville Water used the reservoir until 1879 when the Crescent Hill Reservoir opened. The original reservoir continued as a recreational place and became a swimming pool for the Louisville and Standard Country Clubs. The pool was even used for boating. One writer called the facility "the most magnificent swimming pool in the country." The old reservoir closed in 1935. Today the property is the site of the Veterans Affairs Medical Center.

A MONUMENTAL JOB

Building the original facilities was a slow, backbreaking job that stretched over three-and-a-half years. Work on the reservoir began first. Crews cleared away a primeval beech forest and removed stone for the reservoir and pumping station. One contractor advertised for 500 laborers, 50 quarrymen, 50 stone cutters and 40 boys to drive one-horse carts.

CREWS WORK TO BUILD THE ORIGINAL RESERVOIR

WORK ON THE ORIGINAL INTAKE PIPES INTO THE OHIO RIVER, CIRCA 1857

MEN WHO WORKED TO BUILD THE WATER WORKS

BUILDING A LANDMARK

Union Foundry in Louisville built the pumping engines. Two enormous Cornish-beam engines filled the center of the station, each containing a steam cylinder measuring 70 inches in diameter. Three boilers for each engine were in the two matching wings. The engines worked alternately and could each supply six million gallons of water a day. The initial equipment operated for nearly fifty years and was dismantled in 1911.

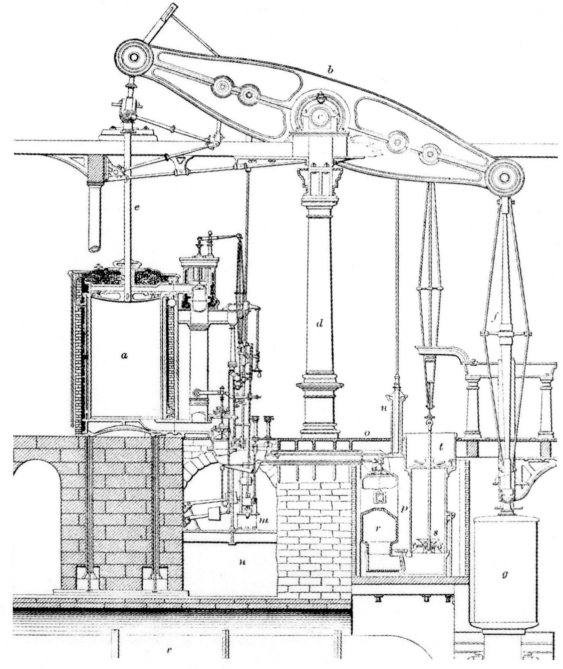

Drawing of the Cornish Pumping engine

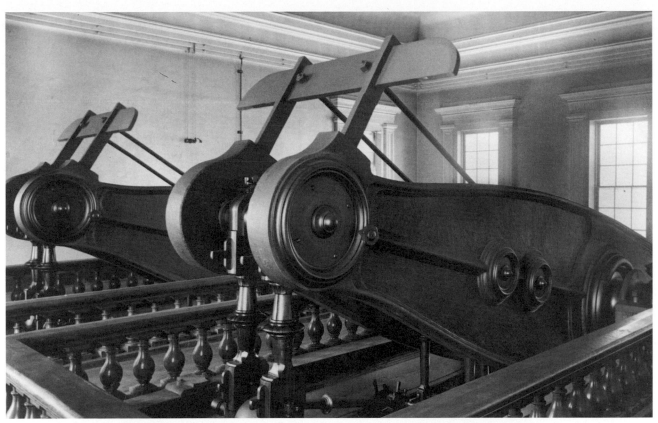

THE BEAMS OF THE CORNISH ENGINES ABOVE, WEIGHED 42 TONS. ONE ENGINEER DESCRIBED THEM AS TAKING UP
"PRACTICALLY EVERY SQUARE FOOT OF SPACE" IN THE CENTER OF THE PUMPING STATION.

FOUR CAST-IRON COLUMNS SUPPORTED THE BEAMS OF THE ENGINE.
THE PUMP ROOM EXTENDED 45 FEET BELOW THE MAIN FLOOR.

In addition to the Pumping Station, tower and reservoir, the Water Works included 26 miles of cast iron pipe. The largest was a 30-inch water main from the station to the reservoir. The total cost to build the works was $829,455.

Scowden declared the water works a "full and complete success" and submitted his resignation, effective December 31, 1860.

A WORKER SITS ATOP THE ORIGINAL 30-INCH CAST IRON WATER MAIN THAT EXTENDED FROM THE PUMPING STATION TO THE RESERVOIR.

HORSES UNLOAD COAL FOR THE BOILERS, CIRCA 1865

Over 600 people helped build the Water Works. Some of the company's earliest employees gather for a photo.

THEODORE SCOWDEN
(1815-1881)

Theodore Scowden was an inventor and engineer. He was born in Pittsburgh, Pennsylvania, in 1815 and was educated in Kentucky at Augusta College. Scowden invented the first revolving breech-loaded firearm at age 23. He had a long career in the water industry, serving as an engineer for the Cincinnati Water Works and designing the Cleveland Water Works before coming to Louisville. Upon completing his work with Louisville Water Company, he oversaw the extension of the canal at the Falls of the Ohio.

WATER, WATER!

Louisville's population in 1860 was roughly 68,000, but just a small number signed up for water: only 512 customers. People didn't use much water, and the wells and cisterns provided a free supply. *The Louisville Daily Courier* announced the water would be turned on at 1p.m. on October 16. The newspapers of the day made little mention about the Water Works, but announcements were published from plumbers offering to bring water pipes into dwellings, stores and factories.

One week later the *Louisville Daily Journal* declared the Water Works complete, stating that it had received its first "aquatic installment."

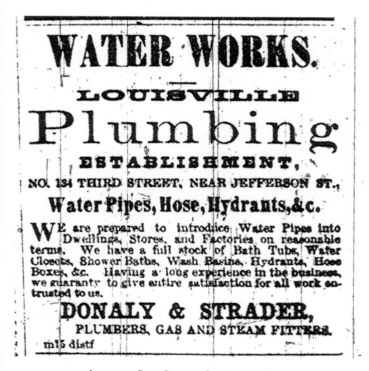

LOUISVILLE DAILY JOURNAL, OCTOBER 16, 1860

At first, the company grew at a slow pace. In 1862, Louisville Water Company had just over 1,000 customers that included lots of private baths, stores and other commercial establishments , but only 293 homes.

SCHEDULE No. 10.

List of Water Consumers supplied by the Works, up to January 1st, 1862.

Boarding houses	22	Hospitals (Military)	6
Bakeries	7	Livery Stables	7
Baths—private	161	Odd Fellows Hall	
Baths—public	42	Paper Mill	1
Barber shops	7	Pork Houses	3
Breweries	6	Petty steam engines	14
Banks	4	Printing offices	5
Candle factory	1	Planing Mill	1
Churches	2	Residences (private)	293
Court-house	1	Restaurants	5
Dye-houses	3	Rolling Mill	1
Flouring Mills	2	Stores	106
Fountains	5	Sprinkling hose-plugs (private)	322
Fish stall	1	do for water carts	11
Gas Works	1	Stock yard	1
Hotels	5	Tobacco Factories	7
Hospital (City)	1	Woolen Factories	2

MORE THAN JUST A DRINK

—◆—

Even if the citizens of Louisville did not quickly take to the Water Works, they certainly benefited from its presence. A drinking fountain for the public was placed in front of the Court House. Perhaps the most obvious benefit, however, was keeping down the dust on the crowded dirt streets. One of the most sought-after

---

Louisville Water Company,

189—
1900   To Louisville Tramway Sprinkler Co.,   Dr.

DATE.	NUMBER OF ORDER.	ARTICLES.			
Feb 5		For street sprinkling from July 15, to Nov. 1, 1899, 3-1/2 mos. at $ 4.00,		$ 14 00	

CORRECT AS ORDERED,
Chas H Findlay
Chief Engineer and Sup't.

ABOVE ITEMS RECEIVED,
Store-house Keeper.

APPROVED BY BOARD OF DIRECTORS,
Feb. 5, 1900.   189—

APPROVED,
Chas R Long
President.

RECEIVED, _Fourteen_ _00/100_ _____ Dollars.

Date _Feby 15th 1900_ _Louisville Tramway Spr Co Pr Jas Wiener_

LOUISVILLE TRAMWAY SPRINKLER COMPANY PAID $14.00 FOR 3.5 MONTHS OF STREET SPRINKLING

OPPOSITE PAGE: ANYONE NEED WATER? HORSE-DRAWN SPRINKLER WAGONS WERE A COMMON SIGHT, JUST AFTER LOUISVILLE WATER COMPANY BEGAN.
UNIVERSITY OF LOUISVILLE / LOUISVILLE WATER COMPANY

LICENSED SPRINKLERS WERE A COMMON SIGHT IN LOUISVILLE

services by the mid-1800s was "street sprinkling." The water company would issue a contract to companies or individuals to water the streets.

Fire protection was a driving force to build a water works. Louisville had suffered two major fires, one in 1827 and the "Great Fire" of 1840. A city ordinance required those who made more than $40 a year to keep two leather buckets filled with water to help with "bucket brigades." In 1858, the Steam Engine Fire Department of Louisville was organized, two years prior to the water company. Within a year into operations, Louisville Water began its role in fire protection. By December of 1861, the company had connected pipes to fill 100 cisterns for fire protection. Water crews would also bore a hole in a main for the fire department to access water and then put a plug in the main. Louisville Water installed its first fire hydrants in 1864 and, by 1936, the company

EARLY FIRE HYDRANTS

MR. DILLINGHAM'S LETTER

had assumed the maintenance for hydrants. Louisville Water now maintains over 22,000 public fire hydrants in its distribution system.

Even if customers didn't drink the water, they did appreciate the energy behind the pressure. A letter from Mr. Dillingham in 1880 asks that the water company move a water meter so he can use the pressure from the water main to power the motor for his pipe organ. It seems the organ was not bellowing to Mr. Dillingham's liking. The letter even includes a diagram for explanation. In the company's minutes, President Chas Long noted the request was referred to a superintendent.

Louisville's Water Works helped industry along the river, providing pressure for hydraulic elevators to reach the top floors of the grain warehouses. The owner of a barber shop asked for water to power a hydraulic fan for the

CROWDS STAND AROUND A BROKEN WATER MAIN

"bath-room" in his business. In another letter, a business owner asks for a larger water main to accommodate a new hydraulic elevator coming from Chicago. The customer complains that his current elevators are so slow that people will not use them and that "our people must be as brisk as the citizens of other western cities." The water company agreed to the larger main.

Louisville's Water Works could also provide a source of entertainment. Crowds of people would gather when crews worked by hand to install the large cast iron pipes in the ground or when one of them broke.

PHOTOGRAPH BY LARRY SPITZER, OCTOBER 18, 1960, COURTESY OF *THE COURIER-JOURNAL*.

CHILDREN ENJOYING THE WATER FROM A MAIN BREAK ON STILZ AVENUE, OCTOBER, 1960

MORE THAN JUST A DRINK

THIS WATER DEPOSIT TICKET GUARANTEED A
SUPPLY OF WATER TO YOUR HOME OR BUSINESS.

HOW MUCH FOR A GALLON?

———— ◆ ————

LOUISVILLE WATER Co. OFFICIALS 1913
1 JOHN S. MORRIS AUDITOR, 2 CHARLES S. POTTER BUYER – ASS'T TREAS.
3 JOHN H. WIEST ENGINEER, 4 J. BAXTER KREMER CHIEF ASSESSOR, 5 THEO.
A. LEISEN CHIEF ENGINEER + SUP'T. 6 BENJ. N. GROSVENOR 1st ENGN'R.
7 CHAS. F. GRAINGER PRES. OF BOARD 8 WM. O. HEAD MAYOR 9 CALVIN M.
DUKE ASS'T. CHIEF ENG'R + ASS'T. SUP'T. 10 LEWIS R. McCLEERY SEC'Y.

When Louisville Water Company began in 1860, no meters measured the amount of water used and the company did not send customers a bill. Instead, the company developed a "tariff" payment schedule. If you were interested in water, the assessor visited your home or business to calculate the annual rate: $5 for a house

THE 1860 TARIFF SCHEDULE WAS RECORDED
IN THE COMPANY'S MINUTES.

with one or two rooms and $3 for each additional family in the house; $1 for every cow owned, as well as $1 for each horse and buggy; $5 for a barber shop with one chair; 10 cents for each barrel of liquor at a distillery. Customers signed a deposit and received a discount for "prompt payment."

By 1873, the water company divided the city into two districts, the East and West. "East" customers paid their bills in January and July; those in the "West" district paid in April and October. The company could turn off the water if a customer did not pay at all by mid-January of each year. Jailer A.E. Camp wrote the company in 1875, saying the inmates of the jail "earnestly implored this Company not to shut off the supply of water." The jail hadn't paid a water bill in two years and owed $1,776. The water company worked out a deal: a cash payment of $395.10 and a note for the remainder.

Company directors kept this handwritten note in 1880 from G.W. Ronald asking for a rebate on his water rent. Mr. Ronald's wife had been ill and "for more than 18 months I have had neither cooking or washing done at my residence."

1875 LETTER FROM JAILER A.E. CAMP

1880 LETTER FROM G.W. RONALD

Measuring the amount of water used was difficult without a meter. Early on, businesses, primarily manufacturers, were the first to get meters, but 151 saloons had meters by 1887.

Many business customers were shocked at the charges and the amount of water they used. The Bremaker Moore paper mill threatened to sue the water company in the late 1870s over the price of water. As a result, Louisville Water began to discount rates for large amounts of usage.

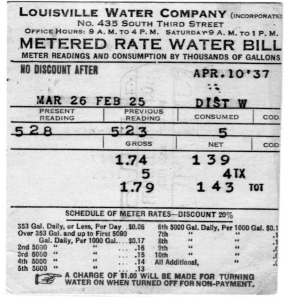

1937 WATER BILL

The company completed the task of metering all its customers by 1941, just before the United States entered World War II. When a large number of the company's workforce was called to active duty, Louisville Water could only read the meters every other month. In 1944, customers began receiving a bi-monthly bill, a practice that continues today. Louisville Water also offered a 50 percent discount on water used on Victory Gardens during the war. In an overwhelming response, 3,500 customers signed up to receive a discount for their "Victory Gardens."

LOUISVILLE WATER COMPANY "VICTORY GARDENS" AD

Customers began receiving a "computerized" bill in 1965 when the company purchased its first mainframe computer, an IBM 1401.

1965 LOUISVILLE WATER COMPANY NEWSLETTER

OPPOSITE PAGE: METER READERS WORKED IN TEAMS IN THE 1960S. EDWARD KEHL AND GILBERT BRUTSCHER (KNEELING) DEMONSTRATE FOR A COMPANY NEWSLETTER.

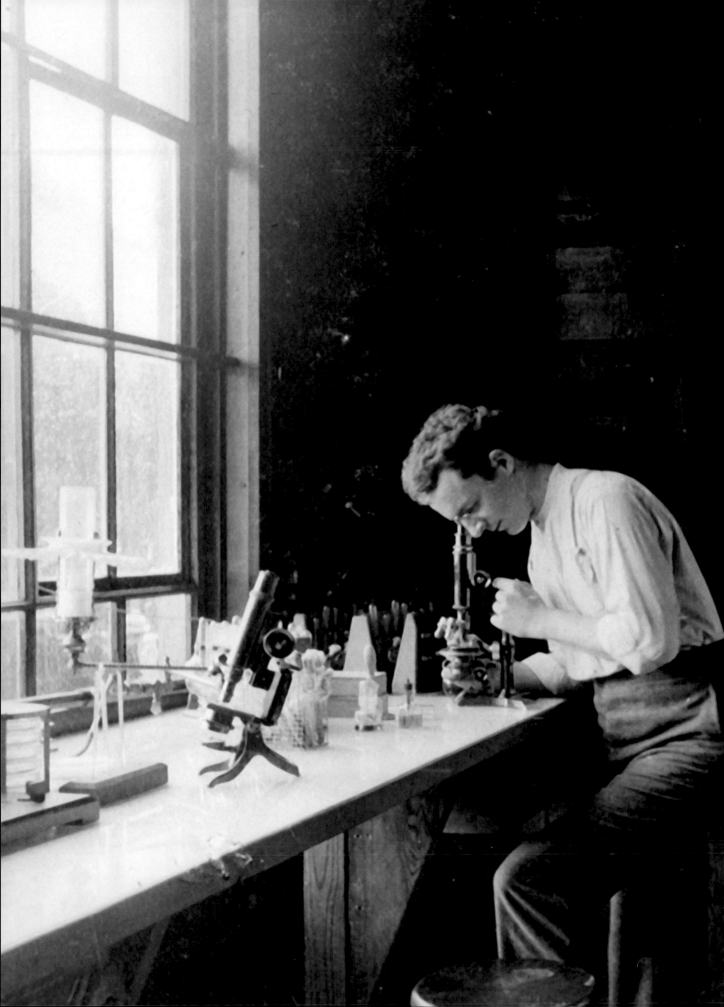

QUEST FOR PURE WATER

Louisville was in a water dilemma at least 40 years before Louisville Water Company began. In 1819, Dr. Henry McMurtrie called the well water "extremely bad" and suggested a steam engine might bring a more wholesome supply of water from the Ohio River. He dubbed the city "graveyard of the west" because of the prevalence of disease, primarily typhoid and cholera.

There were at least six attempts to get a city water provider before Louisville Water finally succeeded in 1860. The first recorded was June 3, 1831, when Louisville's Common Council considered a proposal from a group of local businessmen. Two weeks later, the council rejected the idea on the grounds that water service should be a public, and not a private operation.

Nearly a year later the Common Council began its own attempt to build a water works with James Guthrie, one of Louisville's most influential civic leaders, who was charged with finding a site. The city spent $30,000 to purchase a plot bordered by Main, Preston, Market and Shelby Streets, known as "the mound property," for the water works. Albert Stein, who a year earlier had completed the water works in Richmond, Virginia, was hired as the engineer, and the city authorized advertising for castings and contracts for construction. In 1834, Stein submitted his plans and drawings that suggested another site, and the city purchased additional land. However, it appears a troubled economy and public opposition intervened. In October, 1834, the council defeated a motion to have the public vote to authorize a loan of $200,000 for the water works. Council members may have feared the public would vote against the water works, or the financial situation at the time may have made a public vote a moot point. In either case, the city later began selling plots of land from "the mound property."

Louisville's third attempt came in 1838 with the incorporation of the Louisville Gas & Water Company. The private company's charter was broad, giving it the right to provide gas for lighting Louisville's streets, to erect a water works and to have banking privileges. Two years into operations, a committee of citizens, formed at the request of the government, rejected the Gas & Water Company's attempts to provide water. The committee instead urged the city to build the water works.

Acting upon the committee's recommendation, the Kentucky Legislature approved a fourth attempt by passing an act in January, 1842, authorizing the city to "erect Water Works" and to borrow $200,000 for its construction. A meeting of citizens recommended the city proceed, but selling bonds must have been difficult. Five years later, a report to the Council stated "(t)he $100,000 Water Bonds were counted and burned in the presence of the Mayor and council on 1st March 1847."

Opposite page: Louisville Water Laboratory, circa 1896

By 1850, after four attempts to supply water, Louisville had grown to be the 11th largest city in the United States, with a population of 43,194 people. The river town, a mercantile hub, was also a growing industrial center. The city, a regional leader in meat packing and iron works, led the nation in the manufacture of hemp rope and bags for the southern cotton markets. This growing nineteenth-century city needed a plentiful supply of pure water. Even though the public's health was a factor, it wasn't the most obvious need for water. Businesses and the markets needed larger amounts of water to sustain and grow. Industries needed softer water from the river for their boilers, not the hard water found in ground water wells. The city also needed water for fire protection. The dense population and wooden buildings meant more frequent and devastating blazes.

In a series of articles printed in 1852 in the *Louisville Democrat,* the author wrote about the need for water works, not for drinking, but "to give us a cleansing agent in our houses, in our streets: and a resort ever ready in time of fire." In 1853, the city tried once again to build water works, along with many other civic projects, but the citizens rejected the idea.

Finally, in 1854, the Kentucky Legislature incorporated Louisville Water Company and gave the private company the power to raise capital through sales of shares of stock at $100 each. The end of a 30-year attempt was just a small mention in the newspaper.

The city's government, which had twice before rejected

THE *DAILY COURIER* ON MARCH 6, 1854, INCLUDED A SMALL MENTION OF THE STATE LEGISLATURE'S INCORPORATING LOUISVILLE WATER COMPANY.

private proposals, tried one more time to get the public's approval for water works but with no success.

By 1856, it looked as if Louisville Water Company would end in financial failure. The company could not sell its capital stock; only 51 shares were sold. Original investors included prominent citizens such as William Belknap, Curran Pope and James Speed.

The city wanted to save Louisville Water and launched an education campaign. Leaders stressed the importance of the water to manufacturing. *The Louisville Evening Bulletin* ran articles that stressed the importance of water to fire protection and cleaning the streets and alleys.

Original share of stock for Louisville Water Company

On January 19, 1856, voters approved the ordinance allowing city ownership in Louisville Water Company and, a few months later, the city purchased 5,550 shares of stock. Shortly before construction was complete, another vote authorized the purchase of an additional 2,200 shares.

The Board of Water Works was created in 1906, at which time the city acquired the last of the 51 shares of stock sold to individuals some 40 years earlier. This ended the debate whether the company was a private entity or an agency of the city. This governing body remains today. In the end, the city had become the primary owner of a private corporation with 12,751 shares.

CHARLES HERMANY'S QUEST

If Louisville Water Company's history has a "hero," it is Charles Hermany. He worked alongside the company's first chief engineer, Theodore Scowden, and then assumed that role in 1861. He worked at Louisville Water Company for 50 years, until his death in 1908. Hermany was largely responsible for the original facilities and the pioneering work to develop a clean water supply for Louisville.

The "health" of the water was not a real concern in the beginning. Citizens were using the water for cleaning and the city was really using the Water Works to boost its manufacturing economy. In 1860, Louisville Water did not "treat" the Ohio River water. Most of the mud and sand settled in the seven-million-gallon reservoir. Stories from the time period say you needed to let a cup of water "sit" before drinking it, so the rest of the sediment would settle.

But just a few years into operation, Hermany and President W.F. Barret noted the need for a larger reservoir for additional settling of sediment in the river water.

CHARLES HERMANY'S VISION FOR THE CRESCENT HILL GATEHOUSE, 1876

CRESCENT HILL RESERVOIR

In 1876, Hermany chose a 110-acre plot of farm land in Crescent Hill for a new, 110-million gallon reservoir, more than ten times larger than the first. Men worked alongside horses to remove tons of dirt and rock for a 27-foot embankment around the reservoir. Crews made a deep, narrow cut through a limestone bluff to lay pipe from the pumping station to the reservoir. They created a dirt road on top and named it "Pipe Line Avenue." Today the road is called "Zorn Avenue," named after Louisville Water Company's fourth president, Sebastian Zorn.

LAYING PIPE IN WHAT IS NOW ZORN AVENUE, 1877

CHARLES HERMANY
(1830 - 1908)

Charles Hermany's career revolved around engineering. He was born October 9, 1830, in Lehigh County, Pennsylvania. Hermany had a knack for mathematics and an interest in civil engineering. At age 23, he moved to Cleveland, Ohio, where he received an engineering job with the city and was hired by Theodore Scowden, Louisville Water Company's first chief engineer. Hermany's mark on Louisville Water includes assisting with the original facilities, designing the Crescent Hill Reservoir and Gatehouse, leading the company's groundbreaking work in coagulation and filtration and designing the Crescent Hill Filtration Plant. Ironically, Hermany failed to see his hard work in filtration come to fruition; he caught a cold at a friend's funeral, contracted pneumonia and died on the very day that the first test of the filtration plant was to be made.

Hermany worked at Louisville Water Company for 50 years, but had many other achievements outside of the company. He helped design utilities in Frankfort, Bowling Green and Evansville, Indiana. He also founded the Louisville Engineers and Architects Club and was president for five consecutive terms. Hermany was president of the American Society of Civil Engineers in 1904.

CHARLES R. LONG
(1840 - 1907)

Charles Long, or "Chas" as he was commonly referred to, was president of Louisville Water Company from 1876 until his death in 1907. During his tenure, two notable projects unfolded: the Crescent Hill Reservoir and the landmark experiments into filtration. Long was an entrepreneur. In 1861, he founded the Long & Brother chair manufacturing firm with his older brother. While serving as president of Louisville Water, Long was also president of the city council.

THE CRESCENT HILL GATEHOUSE

Hermany designed the reservoir and the gatehouse that sits in between the basins. The three-story gatehouse was modeled after a similar building Hermany had seen along the Rhine River in Germany.

The building's purpose was to house the valves that controlled the flow of water in and out of the reservoir. But Hermany envisioned combining function with form. His original drawings, from 1876, include Gothic, ornamental details that remain today.

When the reservoir opened in 1879, it provided an abundant supply of water. Louisville Water President Charles Long wanted the facility to be a "pleasant place of attraction to visitors." Today, the reservoir is still part of the water treatment process and Hermany's work remains intact. Some of the original valves still operate, controlling the flow of water into the reservoir. The area around the Crescent Hill Reservoir and Gatehouse remains a popular place for walkers. It was designated a Kentucky Historic Marker site in 2010.

VALVES INSIDE THE GATEHOUSE, CIRCA 1879. THE VALVES REMAIN IN PLACE TODAY.

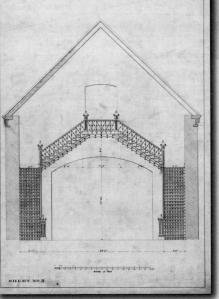

ORIGINAL DRAWING OF THE GATEHOUSE STAIRS, 1876

CHARLES HERMANY'S VISION OF ORNAMENTAL DETAILS TO THE CRESCENT HILL GATEHOUSE APPEAR IN 1876 DRAWINGS AND REMAIN TODAY. ABOVE ARE THE URNS THAT SIT ON EACH CORNER OF THE GATEHOUSE. BELOW IS THE DETAIL ON THE STAIR RAILING THAT LEADS TO THE GATEHOUSE.

PUMPING STATION NO. 2

Hermany's next design was an engineering feat, done with E.D. Leavitt, who would become a well-regarded mechanical engineer. The two designed the "Hermany-Leavitt" steam engine that was installed in Louisville Water Company's second pumping station. Hermany oversaw the design and construction for the station that would sit alongside the original facilities.

Construction began in 1884 and took nine years to complete. In his drawings, Hermany envisioned another community destination. Note below the lady and man and their dog strolling alongside the station and the gentleman fishing on the banks.

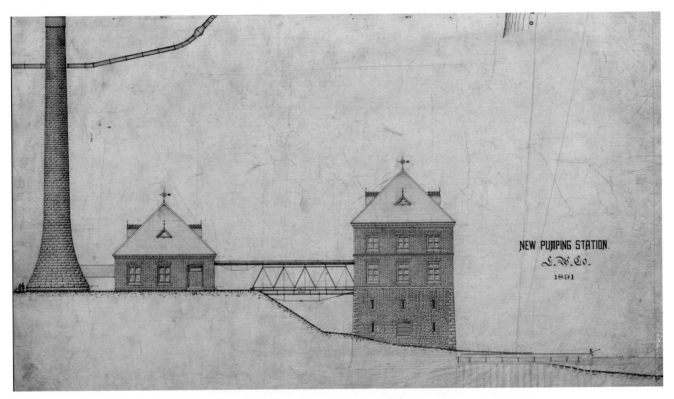

DRAWING FOR PUMPING STATION NO. 2 INCLUDED PEOPLE USING THE GROUNDS FOR RECREATION

The power inside the station was the Hermany-Leavitt pumping engine. It could pump 16 million gallons of water a day and towered 100 feet. The flywheel was 36 feet tall. The engine operated from 1893 to 1928, then was replaced by electric-driven pumps. In 1961, Louisville Water Company dismantled the engine and sold it for scrap. A fully operational model of the engine is on display at the Smithsonian Institution's National Museum of American History in Washington, D.C.

THE HERMANY-LEAVITT PUMPING ENGINE IN STATION NO. 2

PUMPING STATION NO. 1 AND 2, CIRCA 1894

INSTALLING THE HERMANY-LEAVITT PUMPING ENGINE, CIRCA 1892. NOTICE THE LITTLE BOY STANDING ON THE SECOND LEVEL.

GEORGE WARREN FULLER, OBSERVING THE FILTRATION TESTS, CIRCA 1896

One of the companies, the O.H. Jewell Company, also tried a disinfectant. William Jewell, the engineer supervising his company's tests, was not satisfied with the filter results and conducted an experiment using electrolysis to produce chlorine gas from a salt water brine solution. In a letter, company officials asked Jewell to suspend his chlorine experiment, because the results could not be fairly compared to the other filtration experiments. Ironically, Louisville began disinfecting with chlorine in 1914 and the process Jewell developed is similar to technology that Louisville Water uses today to manufacture chlorine.

Shortly after Fuller submitted his report in 1897, Hermany designed the Crescent Hill Filtration Plant with six sand-and-gravel filters, a 25-million-gallon clear well, to store the finished water and a pumping station. It took ten years to build the plant, at a cost of over $1.8 million dollars. Crews also built homes for workers at the plant, and the water company president had a house on the grounds.

In a sad twist of fate, Hermany died of pneumonia on the very day the first plant tests were made. Upon his death, Louisville Water Company noted this in a printed memorial: "Whenever an engineer was asked his opinion about the filter, the response almost invariably was that he was satisfied it would be a success because Charles Hermany had charge of it."

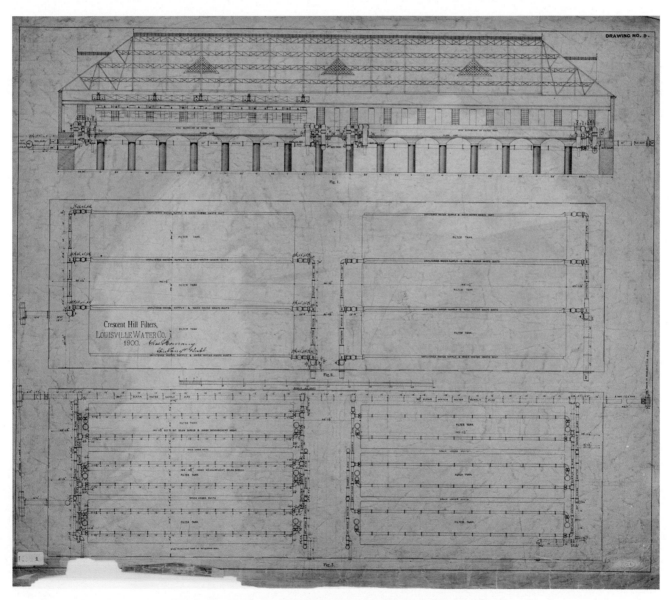

CHARLES HERMANY'S DRAWING FOR THE CRESCENT HILL FILTRATION PLANT, 1900

CONSTRUCTING THE CRESCENT HILL FILTRATION PLANT, CIRCA 1900

When the Filtration Plant opened in July, 1909, newspaper accounts called the construction a "colossal task." The filters removed 99% of the suspended material and bacteria in the water. The Louisville Health Department took note of the success; the death rate from typhoid dropped from 71 per 100,000 people in 1907 to 14 per 100,000 by 1915. When chlorine was finally added as a disinfectant in 1914, disease in Louisville's public drinking water was virtually eliminated.

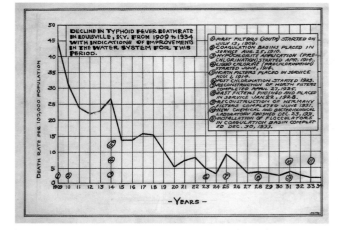

CHART CAPTURING THE DECLINE OF TYPHOID FEVER DEATHS

After the plant opened, Louisville reaped other benefits because of a clean water supply. In 1917, the U.S. Government called the city's water supply "almost perfect" and chose Louisville as the site for Camp Zachary Taylor, a training camp for soldiers.

CRESCENT HILL PUMPING STATION AND FILTER HOUSE

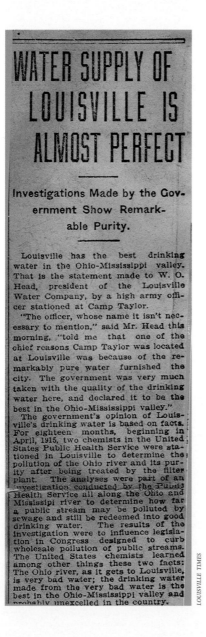

WATER SUPPLY OF LOUISVILLE IS ALMOST PERFECT

Investigations Made by the Government Show Remarkable Purity.

Louisville has the best drinking water in the Ohio-Mississippi valley. That is the statement made to W. O. Head, president of the Louisville Water Company, by a high army officer stationed at Camp Taylor.

"The officer, whose name it isn't necessary to mention," said Mr. Head this morning, "told me that one of the chief reasons Camp Taylor was located at Louisville was because of the remarkably pure water furnished the city. The government was very much taken with the quality of the drinking water here, and declared it to be the best in the Ohio-Mississippi valley."

The government's opinion of Louisville's drinking water is based on facts. For eighteen months, beginning in April, 1915, two chemists in the United States Public Health Service were stationed in Louisville to determine the pollution of the Ohio river and its purity after being treated by the filter plant. The analyses were part of an investigation conducted by the Public Health Service all along the Ohio and Mississippi river to determine how far a public stream may be polluted by sewage and still be redeemed into good drinking water. The results of the investigation were to influence legislation in Congress designed to curb wholesale pollution of public streams. The United States chemists learned among other things these two facts: The Ohio river, as it gets to Louisville, is very bad water; the drinking water made from the very bad water is the best in the Ohio-Mississippi valley and probably unexcelled in the country.

GEORGE WARREN FULLER
(1868 - 1934)

George Warren Fuller's work at Louisville Water Company provided the scientific foundation for water filtration around the world. Born in 1868 in Franklin, Massachusetts, Fuller became a gifted student who graduated from MIT and studied abroad at the Berlin Water Works. His first job was with the Massachusetts State Board of Health, where he spent five years as a biologist studying sewage issues. Louisville Water hired Fuller as a contract researcher in 1895 to perform experiments concerning water purification, giving him the official title of chief chemist and bacteriologist. In 1898, he published his findings in his book, *Report on the Investigation into the Purification of the Ohio River Water at Louisville Kentucky*. Fuller's findings revealed the proficiency of rapid sand filtration and how important the processes of coagulation and sedimentation are prior to filtering.

Fuller went on to advise more than 150 other cities, commissions, and corporations about their water supply and sewage problems. He died in 1934 and today is referred to as the "father of sanitary engineering."

Today, the Crescent Hill Filtration Plant is the state's largest facility of its kind, with the ability to clean and pump over 180 million gallons of water a day. The "Hermany filters" have been replaced with an improved design of sand and coal.

CONSTRUCTING THE WEST SIDE OF THE CRESCENT HILL FILTRATION PLANT, 1907

WEST SIDE OF CRESCENT HILL FILTRATION PLANT, 2010

LOUISVILLE WATER EMPLOYEES PROUDLY DISPLAY AN AWARD FROM THE ENVIRONMENTAL PROTECTION AGENCY.
IN 2005, THE COMPANY RECEIVED THE PARTNERSHIP FOR SAFE WATER 5 YEAR DIRECTOR'S AWARD.

Quality has been a driving force in Louisville Water's history. In 1951, the company was one of the first water utilities in the nation to add fluoride to the drinking water supply. In 1997, Louisville Water became the first utility in the nation to trademark its drinking water and named the product "Pure Tap®." The company distributes empty, refillable bottles to promote the quality and value of tap water.

People often comment on how good Louisville water tastes. In 2008, Pure Tap® was named "best tasting tap water in America" by the American Water Works Association.

EACH YEAR, LOUISVILLE WATER PROVIDES THOUSANDS OF PURE TAP®
BOTTLES TO SCHOOLS, BUSINESSES, SPORTING GROUPS AND INDIVIDUALS.

LOUISVILLE'S WATER TOWER

When the U.S. Government designated the Water Tower and original Pumping Station as National Historic Landmarks in 1971, Secretary of the Interior Rogers C.B. Morton called the tower "one of the finest examples of industrial architecture in the world."

The Water Tower has undergone many changes since 1860. A bit of mystery is also attached to the tower's story.

DEVASTATION

A loud crash roared through the city on March 17, 1890. A tornado snapped the Water Tower from 169 feet to 30 feet. The standpipe and outer wooden shaft lay in pieces on the ground. The base of the tower, which was made of

THE 1890 TORNADO SHATTERED ALL BUT THE BASE OF THE WATER TOWER.

OPPOSITE PAGE: A VISUAL LANDMARK FOR LOUISVILLE WATER COMPANY AND THE COMMUNITY, THE WATER TOWER IS THE OLDEST AND MOST ORNAMENTAL STRUCTURE OF ITS KIND STILL STANDING IN THE UNITED STATES.

PHOTO COURTESY OF TIM MILLS

THE WOODEN CASING OF THE TOWER FELL TO THE GROUND.

WATER WORKS: 150 YEARS OF LOUISVILLE WATER COMPANY

brick, was largely intact, but the land around the Pumping Station and tower was flooded. The two engineers on duty quickly leaped from their posts inside the station and shut off the steam to the Cornish engines. When it fell, the tower also had cut the telephone wire. The two engineers abandoned the station and headed out in a rowboat to the Crescent Hill Reservoir. One of them, John Weist, made a nervous call to Chief Engineer Charles Hermany with the news. "O! Mr. Hermany, this is Mr. Weist. The storm has blown over the standpipe and tower."

No doubt Hermany and others felt an overwhelming sense of loss. The tower was the crowning achievement of the original facilities and crucial to the operation since it dampened the pressure surge of the Cornish pumps. The engines did not operate for six days while Hermany devised an air pump to operate the Cornish engines.

The company began rebuilding the tower in 1891; only the standpipe stood for several years until a new, steel casing was constructed. When finished, it resembled the original with a small modification at the top. Ironically, in 1909, ten years after the work finished, the standpipe was taken out of service.

FOR SEVERAL YEARS AFTER THE TORNADO, THE STANDPIPE DID NOT HAVE AN OUTER CASING. PHOTO ABOVE CIRCA 1896.

MYSTERY

The rebuilding of the Water Tower is when the mystery behind this structure begins. Theodore Scowden's original design of the Water Tower included decorative urns. But in 1861, Charles Hermany described ten statues of gods and goddesses that stood on the original balustrade around the base of the tower. A photograph taken shortly after the tornado indicates that two of the statues survived. One appears to be a woman with a large bonnet.

What happened to those damaged statues remains a mystery. For years, there has also been speculation as to how the current statuary was added. Of particular interest is the choice of an Indian Hunter and his dog placed with Roman and Greek statuary. In its archives, Louisville Water Company suggests different theories: either the Indian statue was chosen to honor the city's past or it was purchased through the connections of a board member. However, in looking through the handwritten notes of the company's minutes, it appears the ten statues were purchased as a group.

Three years after the tornado, Patrick Bannon, who supplied the original terra cotta work for the Pumping Station, proposed ten statues "in first-class order" for $1,700 and lists the ten that are on the tower today. It is not known exactly when the statues, cast at J.W. Fiske Foundry in New York, were installed or how the Indian was offered as part of the group replacement statues.

Whatever the answer, the Water Tower's statues will provide fascination for years to come.

IT APPEARS TWO STATUES SURVIVED THE TORNADO'S WINDS.

TEN STATUES ARE ON THE WATER TOWER TODAY.

Louisville Water Tower Statue Guide

Danaide is one of the fifty daughters of King Danaus of Argos who were married to fifty suitors. As instructed by their father, all but one of them murdered their husbands on their wedding night. As punishment, the Danaides were condemned to an afterlife of unending labor, carrying water in leaky jars from the river Styx, the gateway to the Underworld. Here the Danaide is shown emptying out an urn.

Hebe was the goddess of youth and the cupbearer of the gods. She was often depicted pouring ambrosia from a pitcher. She is identified with the Greek goddess Hebe. Here she is shown pouring a pitcher and holding a cup.

Mercury was the personal messenger of Jupiter, the king of the gods. He was also the god of commerce, science, travel, thievery, persuasion, athletic contests, astronomy, and astrology. He is identified with the Greek god Hermes. Here he is shown wearing a winged cap and holding a flute.

Neptune was the god of the sea, rivers, flood and drought, earthquakes, and horses. He is identified with the Greek god Poseidon. Here he is shown with a trident and a fish.

Flora was the goddess of flowers, a nymph of the Islands of the Blessed. She was the wife of Zephyrus, the West Wind, and the mother of Carpus, fruit. She is identified with the Greek goddess Chloris. Here she is shown with a basket of flowers. This is a replacement statue, cast after Flora was destroyed during a thunderstorm in 1980.

Below are the **Horae**, the goddesses of the seasons and of the natural portions of time. They presided over the revolutions of the heavenly constellations by which the year was measured. They were particularly honored by farmers who planted and tended their crops in time with the rising and setting of the stars—measures of the passing seasons. They are identified with the Greek goddesses the Horai.

Spring is shown with a basket of flowers.

Summer is shown raising one arm and holding a sheath of wheat and a sickle in her left arm.

Autumn is shown holding a grape-filled platter.

Winter is shown wearing a head scarf and fur shirt over her skirt and holding a lamp. cloak and holding a lamp.

The **Indian Hunter and Dog** may have replaced a statue of Diana, the goddess of the moon and the hunt, after the 1890 tornado that destroyed all but two of the original statues. Here he is shown with a dog, while holding a tomahawk and wearing a tobacco-leaf skirt, a beaded necklace around his neck and tobacco leaves in his hair.

The statues and Water Tower have been restored several times since the early 1900s. In 1993, 26 layers of paint were removed from the statuary as part of an extensive restoration. The tower and its statues were repainted again in 2008.

Statues are removed and repainted, 2008

The Water Tower has also survived an attempt to dismantle it. During World War II, the government proposed scrapping the tower for 200 tons of metal. The company resisted and eventually gave a staircase inside the tower to the war effort.

After the tower and original Pumping Station were no longer needed for water production, they sat empty and began to deteriorate. In 1936, Louisville Water Company turned the Pumping Station into a garage. The University of Louisville rented the facility for the Potamological Institute for River Studies in the 1960s. The building was adapted for gallery and office space in the late 1970s for what is now Louisville Visual Art Association.

Thousands of people visit the original Pumping Station and Water Tower every year for festivals, weddings, tours, sporting events and as a backdrop to gaze at the Ohio River. Theodore Scowden and Charles Hermany's vision for a community destination lives on today.

MOTHER NATURE'S POWER

Water is really all in a day's work for a water company, but Louisville Water Company has dealt with its share of "unwanted" water. The Ohio River rushed over its banks quite frequently in the early days. Nevertheless, innovative planning and a little luck allowed the company's operations to continue during the city's most disastrous occasions.

FLOOD WATERS COVER THE GROUNDS IN 1919

OPPOSITE PAGE: FLOOD WATERS RISE AROUND PUMPING STATION NO. 2, CIRCA 1920

1937 FLOOD

For Louisville Water, coal came to the rescue during the worst flood in Louisville's history. When the Ohio River crested on January 27, 1937, at 57.1 feet, the pumping stations were flooded. Louisville Gas & Electric could not provide power to the electric pumps.

Even as employees tried to fire up the steam engines, flood waters filled the boiler area. Pump Station Superintendent Bert Payne reacted quickly to prevent the city from being without water. First, the company asked citizens to ration their supply. Water was only pumped two hours each day from 8-9a.m. and 4-5p.m. Then, Payne devised a plan using a towboat at Pumping Station No.2. The C.C. Slider, along with a barge of coal, pulled next to the station. Crews shoveled coal by hand and one steam pump was put in operation. The operation lasted ten days and Louisville continued to get drinking water throughout the greatest flood in the city's history.

The company took steps to flood-proof the river pumping stations, including installing steel flood-proof doors, raising the ground level around the stations and placing brick over the first floor windows. The year after the flood, President Franklin Roosevelt's Works Projects Administration helped the company improve access to the stations by widening the roadway and raising it to a higher level.

AN EMPLOYEE RESCUES A PIG DURING THE FLOOD

THE HIGH WATER RUSHES INSIDE THE PUMPING STATION
AROUND THE FLYWHEEL

BARGE OF COAL PULLS UP TO THE PUMPING STATION

AN EMPLOYEE OPERATES A PUMP DURING THE
1937 FLOOD.

FLOOD WATERS SURROUND THE SCREEN TOWER

1997 FLOOD

Flood water covered the grounds of the pumping stations again in 1997. This time, crews were lowered from a helicopter to check on the pumps.

1974 TORNADO

Wind, not water, unleashed its fury in the April 3, 1974, tornado. The storm that devastated the region passed directly through the Crescent Hill facilities causing over $1.5 million in damage.

The company's directors described the storm in the annual report: "With a roar said to sound like 'a thousand locomotives' and 'a fury which was beyond belief', the now infamous tornado left behind a twisted and mangled mess…"

The Reservoir and former Gatekeeper's house took the brunt of the storm. Debris from the fairgrounds, approximately 10 miles away, was found near the basin. Some of the original cast-iron fencing was blown over and a water company car along with another ended up in the basin of the reservoir. Over 200 trees were knocked down and scattered across the Crescent Hill grounds.

Power was knocked out for nearly 12 hours to the Crescent Hill facilities. Engineers tried, once again, to use steam power but to no avail. Instead, employees worked through the night to keep the reservoir at capacity to provide adequate supply and pressure for firefighters in the downtown area.

For one of only a handful of times in its history, the

1997 FLOOD

1974 TORNADO DAMAGE

water company asked customers to conserve water. The effort proved counter-productive when customers panicked and instead filled their bathtubs and sinks.

Amazingly, the water company was able to return to normal operations by the morning of April 5, although it took more than a year to finish all the repairs. The company, learning from the disaster, later increased emergency generating capacity at its facilities to deal with future emergencies.

GATEKEEPER'S HOUSE WAS DAMAGED

ORIGINAL FENCING WAS BLOWN OVER

PHOTOGRAPH COURTESY OF DICK TONG, DOUG HARGROVE

THE OLD WATER TOWER AT THE CRESCENT HILL RESERVOIR (SINCE REMOVED) WITHSTOOD THE HIGH WINDS ON APRIL 3. OTHER STRUCTURES AND AUTOMOBILES OBVIOUSLY DID NOT.

BYRON E. "BERT" PAYNE

B. E. Payne was chief engineer and superintendent during some, if not the most, difficult times faced by Louisville Water Company. He began his career at the water company in 1925 as a draftsman, worked his way up the ranks to principal assistant engineer and then in 1941 first assumed the duties of chief engineer and superintendent. Payne was instrumental in the company's response to the 1937 flood and, during World War II, he and his staff worked quickly to supply the water needs of the area's defense plants that seemed to spring up overnight. Payne oversaw the switch from steam to electric pumps, supervised the expansion of the facilities in Crescent Hill, engineered the mergers with eight local water districts and began the planning for the now named B. E. Payne Water Treatment Plant in eastern Jefferson County. Payne retired in 1971, after nearly fifty years of service but remained a consultant. His retirement, however, did not last long. Three years later, with President Horace Estey's sudden death, Payne was brought back to act as interim president. The board did not accept his resignation, until December 31, 1974, three months after the hiring of Foster Burba, as the new president.

B.E. PAYNE TREATMENT PLANT IN PROSPECT IS NAMED AS A TRIBUTE TO PAYNE'S NEARLY 50 YEARS OF SERVICE.

QUALITY WATER ... QUALITY OF LIFE

Louisville Water is known for its quality product. The company is also recognized as an integral part of the community.

A WELCOMING PLACE

The founders described how the facilities would be an open setting for the community; a place where people would want to visit. Residents often wrote letters requesting permission to bring their wagons and carriages to the grounds. Louisville Water employed "Gatekeepers" at the Crescent Hill Reservoir to greet the many visitors often arriving by train. The reservoir grounds were open from 8a.m. to 8p.m. in the summer. The gatekeepers enforced the "rules and regulations" which prohibited bicycles, dogs and those under the influence of "intoxicating liquors." Although Louisville Water no longer employs gatekeepers, the Crescent Hill Reservoir is open every day from dawn to dusk and is a favorite community walking destination.

Even early on, Louisville Water Company was considered a good place to work, employing a number of people as laborers, janitors, engineers and assessors. The crews were called "gangs."

ELLIS HARP MADE $1.75 A DAY AS A LABORER IN 1911.

Opposite page: Trains often stopped with visitors at the Water Works

UNIVERSITY OF LOUISVILLE / LOUISVILLE WATER COMPANY

As the company grew, looking out for its employees and the community became a priority. Directors noted in the 1918 annual report that the company had abolished the job of "blacksmith" when it closed the stable and shop. The blacksmith was then placed in charge of automobile repairs. In World War II, the company used its fleet to garner support for the troops and sold war bonds at the corporate office.

LOUISVILLE WATER COMPANY FLEET CAR

1946 WAR BOND

EMPLOYEES POSE FOR A PICTURE AT THE COMPANY'S 4TH OF JULY PICNIC IN 1909.

In 1860, the company purchased lots on Third Street to build its first office, which would be designed by Gideon Shryock. When concern grew that the building wasn't fireproof, Louisville Water built a new structure in 1910 on Third Street, between Green and Walnut Streets (now Liberty and Muhammad Ali). Once again, the desire was for a community gathering place. The larger building eliminated the long lines for bill paying and included a large, open lobby.

GIDEON SHYROCK DRAWING OF OFFICE FOR LOUISVILLE WATER COMPANY, 1860

COLLECTION OF THE SPEED ART MUSEUM, LOUISVILLE, KENTUCKY

LARGER CORPORATE OFFICE, CONSTRUCTED IN 1910

LOBBY OF CORPORATE OFFICE, 1910

QUALITY WATER ... QUALITY OF LIFE

A METER SHOP WAS ADDED NEXT TO THE CORPORATE OFFICE, CIRCA 1930

A few years later, a meter repair shop and warehouse were added. In 1967, the company added a second switchboard operator because the number of calls had steadily increased.

At LWC switchboard are Blanche Quinn (foreground), a 31-year veteran, and Catherine Tarter.

A 1967 COMPANY NEWSLETTER HIGHLIGHTS THE TWO SWITCHBOARD OPERATORS

The company headquarters remained on Third Street, between Green and Walnut Streets (now Liberty and Muhammad Ali) until 1997. The current offices, just a few blocks south on Third Street at Chestnut, are a tribute to the original facilities. Designed by Louis and Henry Architects, the John L. Huber corporate headquarters includes extensive water details and symbols depicting the Water Tower and smokestack.

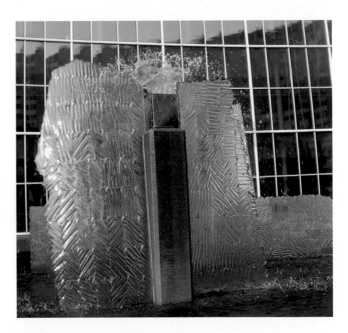

CRESCENT HILL SWIMMING POOL

Louisville Water Company created a popular recreational place when it built the Crescent Hill swimming pool in 1919. President Sebastian Zorn's idea was to create one of the "most beautiful and attractive spots in the country." Admission was 25 cents for adults and 15 cents for children. The price included a locker, bathing suit and towel. The water company reported 40,000 swimmers visited the pool in its first year of operation. The company allowed the U.S. Government to use the pool for one dollar during World War II. Fighter pilots flying into Bowman Field were allowed a private swim. There was a public outcry when the water company announced it would close the pool in the early 1950s to make room for additional treatment facilities. After much debate, the City of Louisville built five community swimming pools, including the present pool near the Crescent Hill Reservoir.

THE FIRST CRESCENT HILL SWIMMING POOL SAT DIRECTLY ACROSS FROM THE GATEHOUSE.

POSTCARD OF THE CRESCENT HILL SWIMMING POOL

THE CRESCENT HILL SWIMMING POOL INCLUDED A FOUNTAIN.

THE POOL INCLUDED A LARGE BATH HOUSE AND DIVING DOCK.

SEBASTIAN ZORN

Sebastian Zorn was the only person to serve as president of Louisville Water Company at two different times, from 1907-1910 and 1918-1919. Zorn was a grain company executive and is credited with creating a "business culture" at Louisville Water. When he died suddenly in December, 1919, the Board of Water Works paid tribute to his service by renaming the stretch of road from the Pumping Station to the Crescent Hill Reservoir Zorn Avenue.

INNOVATION ABOVE AND BELOW

Moving water from place to place requires the right balance of pressure and volume. The original distribution system relied only on gravity to send water through 26 miles of cast iron mains. Today, a complex system of booster pumps, elevated tanks and gravity moves water through over 4,000 miles of water main. Pieces of the pipe laid in 1860 are still in service today along Story Avenue. The cast iron was lined with cement and has stood the test of time. The original cast iron pipes were made by local iron foundries in Louisville, including Union Foundry and the Dennis Long Company. On October 16, 2010, Louisville was recognized by the by the Ductile Iron Research Association for having delivered 150 years of service through an original 20-inch cast-iron water main on Story Avenue.

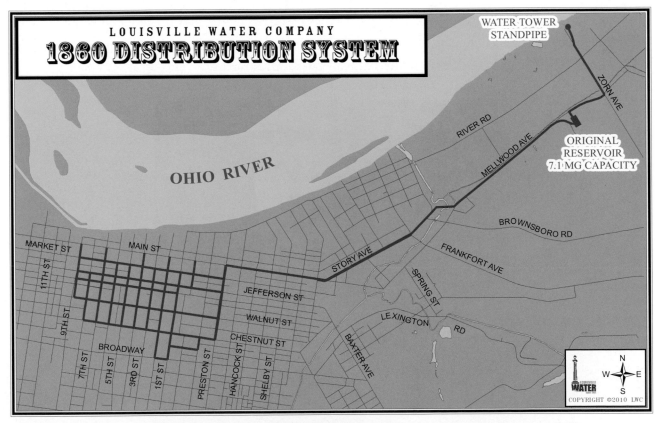

THE RED LINES REPRESENT THE 26 MILES OF PIPE IN LOUISVILLE WATER COMPANY'S ORIGINAL DISTRIBUTION SYSTEM IN 1860.

OPPOSITE PAGE: LAYING HEAVY CAST-IRON PIPE IN THE GROUND WAS SLOW, ARDUOUS WORK. A 48-INCH WATER MAIN STRETCHES OVER BEARGRASS CREEK ALONG WHAT IS NOW KENTUCKY STREET.

UNIVERSITY OF LOUISVILLE / LOUISVILLE WATER COMPANY

Shortly into operations, Louisville Water Company began expanding beyond the city limits. After pleas from residents, the company extended a 16-inch water main to the Portland neighborhood in 1873. The water company employed dozens of laborers to lay pipe, often relying on a pulley system to help lower the heavy pieces into trenches.

Louisville Water Company has expanded service throughout the Louisville region, including Jefferson, Oldham, Shelby, Spencer, Nelson and Bullitt Counties in Kentucky. The service area covers 600 square miles.

Louisville used cast-iron pipe up through the 1960s and then transitioned to ductile-iron pipe in the 1970s. By 1985, the company began to diversify to include ductile iron, PVC, pre-stressed concrete and steel. Originally, water was supplied to homes through small diameter service lines made of lead, then in 1934, Louisville began using copper lines to serve homes.

Piping systems are designed to provide service for 60 to 100 years. In 1985, Louisville Water began developing what would become a model asset management and infrastructure renewal program. One of the largest programs in the country was launched to replace or rehabilitate the original 600 miles of cast-iron pipe and replace 60,000 lead service lines installed before 1935. The original scope of this $150 million program is essentially complete and the program continues today with an annual allocation of $10 million to upgrade aging infrastructure.

INSTALLING WATER MAIN, CIRCA 1935

A LARGE STRETCH OF PIPE INTERSECTED AMONG HOMES AND BUSINESSES WHEN THE COMPANY EXTENDED A WATER MAIN FROM CRESCENT HILL TO DOWNTOWN.
OFTEN THE PIPES SAT ABOVE THE GROUND OR WERE BURIED ABOUT A FOOT DEEP. TODAY, NEARLY ALL WATER MAINS ARE UNDERGROUND.

AN EMPLOYEE STANDS ATOP A LARGE WATER MAIN JUST BEFORE IT IS LOWERED INTO THE GROUND. PHOTO CIRCA 1920.

INNOVATION ABOVE AND BELOW

AN 1860 PIPE SITS AT THE BASE OF THE PUMPING STATION ON THE COMPANY'S 100TH ANNIVERSARY.

On Louisville Water's 100th anniversary, President Neil Dalton and others stood at the base of the Pumping Station in front of one of the 1860 water mains, and then invited guests to watch one of the steam engines work.

Shortly after its centennial anniversary, Louisville Water began to merge with smaller utilities to form a large metropolitan utility. Some districts were reluctant to give up their independence and some contested the merger in court. Today, the service area includes all of Louisville Metro and parts of the surrounding counties. Louisville Water has become a regional water utility with projects that extend to the south and east in Kentucky.

IN PRESTON STREET DISTRICT . . .
Poll Shows Water Consumers Favor Merger

Some $168,200 in savings would have been realized by the customers of the Preston Street Road Water District had their district been merged with the Louisville Water Company last year.

This figure represents an average of $17 per family, according to Glenn Rhoades, vice-president of the Okolona Junior Chamber of Commerce and chairman of a Jaycee committee organized to further merger plans of the Water District with the Louisville Company.

Immediate results of the merger, Rhoades said, would be a rate reduction of 30-percent plus an immediate refund of $47,000 made directly to the people. This money represents the $5 held as deposit when each customer originally contracted with the Preston Street Water District.

Okolona Jaycees conducted a poll of residents within the Okolona area to determine their feeling on the matter.

A petition presented to these people, accompanied by a fact sheet outlining the proposals involved in the merger, resulted in 99-percent of those polled going on record as favoring the move.

Under the merger proposal, rates would be reduced to current customers of the district from present figures to one equal to 125-percent of that now applied to users within the direct area of the Louisville Water Company.

Figures calculated in the office of the Jefferson County Judge indicate that the average customer within the Preston Street District now pays $4.56 per month and could anticipate a decrease to $2.72 per month.

Readers Favor Merge, Sewer Sinking Fund

Results of The Reporter's poll conducted through last week's paper were as follows:

	YES	NO	UNDECIDED
Water Company Merger	80%	20%	–
Sinking Fund for Sewers	60%	40%	–
Passage of School Tax	40%	50%	–

	JOHNSON	GOLDWATER
For President	50%	50%

A recent rate reduction within the district was calculated to reduce average residential rates approximately $5 per year, but Rhoades said that the monthly payments were reduced very slightly because the minimum usage rate was increased from 3,000 gallons per month to 4,000.

* * *

Dr. William Penney, a commissioner of the district, told Rhoades that a meeting held three weeks ago resulted in negotiations being settled with the exception of one point.

That specific point involves whether or not water users could expect to eventually be placed on the same rate schedule as that now enjoyed by current L.W.C. customers.

Horace W. Estey, president of the Louisville Water Company, told The Reporter that another meeting will be held in the near future to discuss the matter, but that he was not free to make any statement at this time regarding the rate schedule.

A study which was released last December concerning the operation of L.W.C. suggested that rates to individual water districts be increased 33-1/3-percent. A growth factor confronts the company in that it is surrounded by the districts and cannot expand.

The innovation in producing and delivering water has evolved in the last 150 years. Company reports did not mention paying a laboratory staff until the filtration experiments in 1896. The water quality area has expanded over the years to now include a lab certified by the Environmental Protection Agency, with scientists performing over 200 tests daily on the drinking water supply.

1896 LAB

1954 LAB

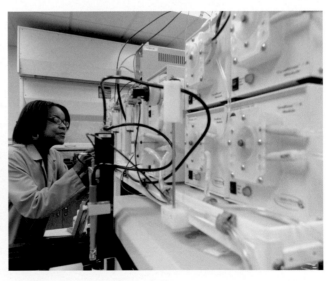

2010 LAB

Today, the innovation continues deep in the ground, next to the Ohio River. Louisville Water Company is the first water utility in the world to combine a tunnel with gravity-fed wells as a source for drinking water. The sand and gravel 100 feet in the ground filter the ground water. The project is a natural extension of Charles Hermany's vision for filtration some 100 years ago, only this time the process is underground.

SITE OF THE RIVERBANK FILTRATION PROJECT.

A GEOLOGIST WALKS THROUGH THE RIVERBANK FILTRATION TUNNEL.

REMEMBRANCES

John L. Huber, president, Louisville Water Company, 1991-2007

JOHN HUBER

John Huber spent his entire professional career at Louisville Water Company starting as a co-op student in 1964. Four years later he was hired full-time, worked his way to become chief engineer and then president. When he retired in 2007, Huber had spent 44 years at Louisville Water, 16 years as president. The company's current headquarters bears Huber's name, as a tribute to his work.

Huber was, and still is, a student of the company's history. He recalled a few stories for this book.

WEATHER AND WATER

Mother Nature was not kind to the Louisville area in the 1970s. The tornado of 1974, remembered by many for its destructive power, wreaked havoc on the Crescent Hill Filtration Plant. The plant, constructed with thick walls to withstand such a windstorm, was relatively undamaged, but all the power to the facilities was lost. Huber recalled that, "the tornado took out all the power lines to the Crescent Hill Water Treatment Plant. The electrical substation by Grinstead Drive was destroyed. The pumps cannot work without power. LG&E worked all night and had the power back on by the next morning. They did a heck of a job."

Huber recalled the fury of the storm that could have been disastrous for workers at the Crescent Hill Reservoir. "Two workers were just finishing replacing the round window over the door of the Gatehouse," Huber began, "when the storm came up on them. They found a safe spot inside the building to wait out the storm. They didn't have time to move their truck and left it on the walk on top of the embankment, just in front of the building. After the storm passed, they came out and the truck was gone. They couldn't find it and didn't know what happened to it until the reservoir was drained. There was the truck." Another near disaster was the resident engineer's trailer. "The trailer was gone," Huber said, "just gone. All the records, all the drawings... nothing was left. Not long after the storm, we received a call from a farmer in Carrollton saying he had found in his field a drawing with 'Louisville Water Company' on it."

THE TORNADO THREW A TRUCK FROM LOUISVILLE PLATE GLASS AND LOUISVILLE WATER COMPANY INTO THE RESERVOIR

THE WINDS TURNED OVER PART OF THE STONE BALUSTRADE, DATING BACK TO 1878

Cold weather is a yearly concern for water companies. "Really cold weather wreaks havoc on a water system," Huber explained. "In the summer the river temperature can be in the 80s, in the winter the water temperature is 35 to 40 degrees. It's the expansion and contraction of the pipes that causes them to break. At 38 degrees you can count on it like clockwork." During the winter of 1977/78 the Ohio River froze over, with the temperature dipping to -20 degrees. Suspended ice particles in the water froze on the river intake screen almost stopping the flow of water. "There were many breaks," Huber recounted, "both in the mains, which are very difficult to thaw, as well as over 1,000 service lines, which sometimes froze again after they were thawed." The old paper ticket system in use at the time for service requests was overwhelmed and led to a chaotic situation. The crisis resulted in the development of a new service ticket system to improve the company's ability to respond to customer requests.

DEDICATED EMPLOYEES

Huber worked with two presidents at Louisville Water. When he began his career, Horace Estey was the company's president. Huber credits Estey and the "positive, can-do atmosphere" he created that led to the sometimes turbulent, yet ultimately successful expansion of the company's reach into all of Jefferson County and beyond. Foster Burba next assumed the presidency.

HORACE ESTEY
PRESIDENT
1963-1974

PEOPLE WALKING ON THE FROZEN OHIO RIVER IN THE WINTER OF 1977-78

FOSTER BURBA
PRESIDENT
1974-1991

Burba's presidency was marked with financial concerns. The debt incurred from the mergers and updating and expanding the physical plant threatened the long term health of the company. Huber described Burba as a great business leader. Under his leadership, the debt was refinanced several times, giving the company more cash on hand. Anticipating current and future needs, Burba was also active in the American Water Works Association, serving as the national president in 1992. He also worked to create a water industry presence in Washington, D.C., which in turn helped to set safety standards.

Huber credits the dedicated employees at Louisville Water for continuing the tradition set 150 years ago. The company has a cooperative partnership with its union, Local 1683 of the American Federation of State, County and Municipal Employees, which constitutes nearly half of the workforce. Huber recalled how when the partnership was developed, the company better utilized the talents of its union and offered improved customer service.

The relationship between the company and the Local has been praised nationally for its business model and won numerous awards.

UNION CREWS WORKING IN THE FIELD

AFTERWORD

THE CRESCENT HILL RESERVOIR AND GATEHOUSE

As Louisville Water Company progresses into the next chapter of its history, it is interesting how the original themes of the company resonate today. Clearly, Theodore Scowden and Charles Hermany envisioned a water works where quality was evident in both the product and the facilities. The founders engineering feats created the foundation for the company's success. The original facilities still tower on the banks of the Ohio River. The innovative ideas with filtration and disinfection continue to provide the community with a safe supply of drinking water every day.

From its beginning, Louisville Water Company has always seen itself as part of the community. In the early years, it built a park near the river, entertained visitors at the Reservoir and constructed a swimming pool for the public. Today, that sense of community includes hosting tours of the original facilities, visiting classrooms with science programs, and partnerships to improve the health of children and adults.

Water "works" in so many ways throughout this community.

LOUISVILLE WATER COMPANY PRESIDENTS AND CHIEF ENGINEERS, 1856 – 2010

PRESIDENT		CHIEF ENGINEER	
1856 - 1863	Albert Harris	1857 - 1860	Theodore Scowden
1864 - 1873	William Barret	1861-1908	Charles Hermany
1874 – 1907	Charles Long	1908	S. Bent Russell
1907 – 1909	Sebastian Zorn	1908-1913	Theodore Leisen
1910 – 1913	Charles F. Grainger	1914-1920	James B. Wilson
1914 – 1917	W. O. Head	1921-1937	John Chambers
1918 - 1919	Sebastian Zorn	1937-1941, 1946	L.S. Vance
1919 – 1921	Henry O. Gray	1941	B.E. Payne (Acting Chief Engineer)
1922 – 1926	George Weissinger Smith	1942 – 1971	B. E. Payne
1927 – 1933	Edward Miller	1971 – 1990	Frank Campbell
1934	Harry Volz	1990	John L. Huber
1935 – 1937	Joseph Scholtz	1991 – 2007	Greg C. Heitzman
1937 – 1959	Henry Gerber	2007 – present	James Brammell
1959	William Tate (Acting President)		
1960 - 1962	Neil Dalton		
1963 - 1974	Horace Estey		
1974	B. E. Payne (Acting President)		
1974 - 1991	Foster Burba		
1991 - 2007	John L. Huber		
2007 - present	Greg C. Heitzman		

LOUISVILLE WATER COMPANY
BOARD OF WATER WORKS

LOUISVILLE WATER COMPANY
EXECUTIVE LEADERSHIP TEAM

PHOTO CREDITS

Page 8
Louisville Water Company Collection (ULPA 1984.20.116) Special Collections, University of Louisville

BUILDING A LANDMARK

Page 10
Louisville Water Company Collection (ULPA 1984.20.668), Special Collections, University of Louisville

Page 16
Louisville Water Company Collection (ULPA.1984.20.186), Special Collections, University of Louisville

Page 17
Krementz Collection (ULPA 1989.14.11), Special Collections, University of Louisville

Krementz Collection (ULPA 1989.14.09), Special Collections, University of Louisville

Page 19
Louisville Water Company Collection (ULPA 1984.20.270), Special Collections, University of Louisville

Louisville Water Company Collection (ULPA 1984.20.165), Special Collections, University of Louisville

MORE THAN JUST A DRINK

Page 26
Louisville Water Company Collection (ULPA 1984.20.119), Special Collections, University of Louisville

Page 28
Louisville Water Company Collection (ULPA 1984.20.191), Special Collections, University of Louisville

Page 29
Louisville Water Company Collection (ULPA 1984.20.219), Special Collections, University of Louisville

Page 30
Louisville Water Company Collection (ULPA 1984.20.189), Special Collections, University of Louisville

Page 33
Potter Collection (ULPA 12308), Special Collections, University of Louisville

QUEST FOR PURE WATER

Page 45
Louisville Water Company Collection (ULPA 1984.20.175), Special Collections, University of Louisville

Page 49
Louisville Water Company Collection (ULPA 1984.20.43), Special Collections, University of Louisville

Page 50
Louisville Water Company Collection (ULPA 1984.20.43), Special Collections, University of Louisville

Louisville Water Company Collection (ULPA 1984.20.25), Special Collections, University of Louisville

Page 51
Louisville Water Company Collection (ULPA 1984.20.297), Special Collections, University of Louisville

Page 52
Louisville Water Company Collection (ULPA 1984.20.409), Special Collections, University of Louisville

Page 53
Louisville Water Company Collection (ULPA 1984.20.463), Special Collections, University of Louisville

Page 54
Louisville Water Company Collection (ULPA 1984.20.465), Special Collections, University of Louisville

Page 55
Louisville Water Company Collection (ULPA 1984.42), Special Collections, University of Louisville

Page 64
Louisville Water Company Collection (ULPA 1984.20.147), Special Collections, University of Louisville

LOUISVILLE'S WATER TOWER

Page 68
Louisville Water Company Collection (ULPA 1984.20.104), Special Collections, University of Louisville

Louisville Water Company Collection (ULPA 1984.20.109), Special Collections, University of Louisville

ACKNOWLEDGMENTS

Louisville Water Company acknowledges the contributions of the following for their assistance in the production of Water Works: 150 Years of Louisville Water Company.

Greg Heitzman, President and CEO, Louisville Water Company

John Huber, Past President, Louisville Water Company

Photographic Archives in Special Collections, Ekstrom Library, University of Louisville

PHOTOGRAPHY
Howell and Howell Contractors
Tim Mills
Pat Pfister
Pat Propes
Mike Stepp

RESEARCH ASSISTANCE
Terry Conway
James Bates
Marianne Butler
Julian Donahue
Claire Heitzman
Christy Ray
Jeremy Smith
Ashley Sutton
Sam Thomas

EDITING
Adele Lile

Special recognition to Jay Ferguson for his diligence in researching the history of the company and his pursuit to uncover stories and photographs for this book.